GW00870155

Chemistry 1a — Products from Rocks

Page 1 — Atoms and Elements

Q1 a) zero
b) ion
c) protons, electrons (in either order)
d) negatively

Q2

Particle	Charge
Proton	+1
Neutron	0
Electron	-1

Q3 a) nucleus
b) electron
c) proton
d) neutron
e) proton

Q4

Diagram should be correctly labelled as above
Q5 copper and oxygen should be circled

Page 2 — The Periodic Table

Q1 a) A group in the periodic table is a **vertical** line of elements.
b) Most of the elements in the periodic table are **metals**.
c) There are about 100 different **elements** in the periodic table.
d) Non-metals are on the **right-hand** side of the periodic table.
e) Elements in the same group have **similar** properties.
f) The symbol for chlorine is **Cl** and the symbol for potassium is **K**.

Q2 a)

b) 11
c) 11
d) 23 – 11 = 12
Q3 a) The following should be ticked: **A** and **D**
b) Sodium and potassium are both in Group I, so they both contain the same number of electrons in their outer shell. The properties of elements are decided by the number of electrons they have in their outer shell.
Q4 a) false
b) false
c) true
d) true
e) true

Pages 3-4 — Electron Shells

Q1 a) i) true
ii) false
iii) false
iv) false
b) ii) The lowest energy levels are always filled first.
iii) Atoms are most stable when they have full outer shells.
iv) Reactive elements have partially filled outer shells.

Q2 E.g. The inner most electron shell should be filled first / there should be two electrons in the inner shell; The outer shell contains too many electrons, it only holds a maximum of 8 electrons.
Q3 a) 2,2
b) 2,6
c) 2,8,4
d) 2,8,8,2
e) 2,8,3
f) 2,8,8
Q4 a) Noble gases are unreactive elements because they have full outer shells of electrons.
b) Group I metals are reactive elements, because they have an incomplete outer shell of electrons.
Q5 a) 2,8,7
b)

c) Its outer shell isn't full (it's keen to get an extra electron).
Q6

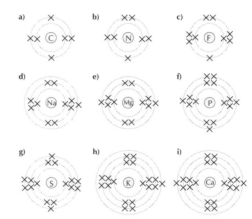

Page 5 — Compounds

Q1 a) true
b) true
c) true
d) true
Q2 Missing words are: ions, positive, negative, attracted, ionic, molecules, covalent.
Q3 a) ionic
b) 1
c) +1
d) NaCl
Q4 Sharing electrons allows both atoms to achieve the stable 'full outer shell' of electrons. They form covalent bonds.

Pages 6-7 — Balancing Equations

Q1 a) Correctly balanced
b) Incorrectly balanced
c) Incorrectly balanced
d) Correctly balanced
e) Correctly balanced
f) Correctly balanced
Q2 The third equation should be circled.
Q3 a) The reactants are methane and oxygen, and the products are carbon dioxide and water.
b) methane + oxygen → carbon dioxide + water
c) $CH_4 + 2O_2 \rightarrow CO_2 + 2H_2O$
Q4 a) $2Na + Cl_2 \rightarrow 2NaCl$
b) $4Li + O_2 \rightarrow 2Li_2O$

Chemistry 1a — Products from Rocks

c) $MgCO_3 + 2HCl \rightarrow MgCl_2 + H_2O + CO_2$
d) $2Li + 2H_2O \rightarrow 2LiOH + H_2$
Q5 a) $CuO + 2HBr \rightarrow CuBr_2 + H_2O$
b) $H_2 + Br_2 \rightarrow 2HBr$
c) $2Mg + O_2 \rightarrow 2MgO$
d) $2NaOH + H_2SO_4 \rightarrow Na_2SO_4 + 2H_2O$
Q6 a) $3NaOH + AlBr_3 \rightarrow 3NaBr + Al(OH)_3$
b) $2FeCl_2 + Cl_2 \rightarrow 2FeCl_3$
c) $N_2 + 3H_2 \rightarrow 2NH_3$
d) $4Fe + 3O_2 \rightarrow 2Fe_2O_3$
e) $4NH_3 + 5O_2 \rightarrow 4NO + 6H_2O$

Pages 8-12 — Using Limestone

Q1 calcium carbonate
Q2 a) calcium oxide, carbon dioxide
b) magnesium oxide
c) $CuCO_3 \rightarrow CuO + CO_2$
d) A Bunsen burner would not reach a high enough temperature for the reaction to happen.
Q3 The missing words are: limestone, mortar, concrete.
Q4 a) calcium carbonate $\rightarrow$ calcium oxide + carbon dioxide
b) To neutralise soils that are acidic.
Q5 a) carbon dioxide, water
b) i) magnesium carbonate + sulfuric acid $\rightarrow$ magnesium sulfate + carbon dioxide + water
ii) $MgCO_3 + H_2SO_4 \rightarrow MgSO_4 + CO_2 + H_2O$
c) Any two from, e.g. copper/zinc/calcium/sodium
d) Limestone is mainly calcium carbonate and acid rain is a weak acidic solution. So, when acid rain falls, it reacts with the calcium carbonate to form a salt, carbon dioxide and water. This means that limestone buildings are gradually eroded away by acid rain.
Q6 a) If you make a saturated solution of calcium hydroxide in water (called limewater) and bubble gas through it, the solution will turn cloudy if the gas is carbon dioxide.
b) $Ca(OH)_2 + CO_2 \rightarrow CaCO_3 + H_2O$
Q7 a) Thermal decomposition is when one substance chemically changes into at least two new substances when it's heated.
b) Calcium oxide will react with water to give an alkaline substance. You could prove this using universal indicator (it would turn blue or purple). Calcium carbonate would remain neutral.
Q8 a) The limestone in the Peak District is very pure.
b) About 1.6 million tonnes $(7.9 \div 5 = 1.58)$.
c) It is used in agriculture and burned in lime kilns.
d) Any three from: increased traffic, spoiling the look of the landscape, discouraging tourism, noise, dust, damage to habitats and the environment.
e) i) canals and railways
ii) by road / by lorry
f) Answer will depend on student's opinion, but they are likely to say that they are against it because the article focuses on the problems associated with quarrying rather than the benefits it has.
g)

Use	Percentage	Total amount quarried in tonnes
Aggregate (for road-building etc.)	52%	$(7900000 \div 100) \times 52 = 4108000$
Cement	24%	$(7900000 \div 100) \times 24 = 1896000$
Iron and steel making	2%	$(7900000 \div 100) \times 2 = 158000$
Chemicals and other uses	22%	$(7900000 \div 100) \times 22 = 1738000$

Q9 Granite, paint and bricks should be circled.
Q10a) neutralisation
b) The powdered limestone removes sulfur dioxide from the waste gases.
Q11a) Any two from, e.g. it makes huge holes which permanently damage the landscape / noise / dust / destruction of habitats for plants and animals / transport is usually by lorry causing more noise and pollution / waste material causes unsightly tips.
b) Quarries provide employment for local people which can provide a boost to the local economy. There may also be improvements to infrastructure such as roads, recreational and health facilities.
Q12a) Wood rots, is damaged by insects and is flammable. Concrete is not affected by any of these problems.
b) Metals corrode but concrete doesn't.
c) Bricks are made to a set size and shape but concrete can be poured into moulds of any size and shape.

Pages 13-17 — Getting Metals from Rocks

Q1 a) A metal ore is a mineral which contains enough metal to make it worthwhile extracting the metal from it.
b) oxygen and sulfur
Q2 Gold is less common than iron, which makes it expensive and this means that it is worth extracting it from low-grade ores. Iron is less valuable, and more common, so it is only economic to extract it from high-grade ores.
Q3 a) Year 1
b) cost of extraction = $75/100 \times £2.00 = £1.50$
The cost of mineral extraction was £1.50 in year 6.
Q4 As technology improves, it becomes possible to extract more metal from a sample of rock than before. So it might now be worth extracting metal that wasn't worth extracting in the past.
Q5 Missing words are: carbon, below, reduction, electrolysis, more.
Q6 dekium, bodium, **carbon**, candium, antium
Q7 a) Any one from:
e.g. it is too impure to conduct electricity well. /
The impurities make it too brittle to be used for wires.
b) i) Impure copper (obtained e.g. by reduction with carbon) is purified using electrolysis.
ii) E.g. electrolysis is expensive because it uses a lot of energy.
Q8 Missing words are: electricity, liquid, electricity, positive, electrode.
Q9 Electrolysis is the breaking down of substances using electricity. A molten substance or solution has free ions which conduct the electricity.
Q10 The copper produced will have zinc impurities in it.
Q11a) A — electrodes
B — copper sulfate solution
C — copper ions
b) The impurities are not charged (i.e. they are neutral) so they are not attracted to the cathode.
Q12a) Because iron is more reactive than copper.
b) No, because iron is less reactive than aluminium so it wouldn't be able to push the aluminium out and bond to the sulfate.
Q13 Any two from, e.g. there is a limited supply of copper. There is an increasing demand for copper. Mining new copper is damaging to the environment.
Q14a) Bioleaching uses bacteria to separate copper from copper sulfide. The bacteria get energy from the bond between copper and sulfur, separating out the copper from the ore in the process. The leachate (the solution produced by the process) contains copper, which can be extracted, e.g. by filtering.
b) Phytomining.

Chemistry 1a — Products from Rocks

c) The supply of copper-rich ores is limited and the demand for copper is growing. These alternative methods can extract copper from low-grade ores and from the waste that is currently produced when copper is extracted.

Page 18 — Impacts of Extracting Metals

Q1 Social factors include: new jobs available for locals, improved local services, influx of people might put strain on local services.
Economic factors include: more money in local economy, more goods made from the extracted metal are available.
Environmental factors include: pollution such as dust, noise and emissions from vehicles, habitat destruction, scarring of the landscape, after extraction the area may be turned into a conservation area.

Q2 Aluminium is recycled because it takes a lot of energy to extract it from its ore, so even though it is very common extracting new aluminium is very expensive. Gold is recycled because it is rare and so it's too valuable to throw away.

Page 19 — Properties of Metals

Q1 a) Metal 3 (because it has the best heat conduction, and is strong and resistant to corrosion).

b) Metal 2 (because it is the strongest, isn't too expensive and won't corrode too much). (Accept metal 3.)

c) Metal 1 (because it is most resistant to corrosion so it will last a long time).

Q2 It can be bent to make pipes and tanks, and it doesn't react with water.

Q3 a)

Property	Aluminium	Titanium
Density	**low**	**low**
Strength	low	high
Corrosion resistance	**high**	**high**

b) Titanium (both Ti and Al are corrosion resistant, but it also has to be strong to take a person's weight).

Page 20 — Alloys

Q1 a) A mixture of two or more metals or a mixture of a metal and a non-metal.

b) By adding small amounts of carbon or other metals to the iron.

Q2 a)

Metal / Alloy	What has been added	Use
low-carbon steel	nothing	blades for tools
iron from a blast furnace	chromium	cutlery
high-carbon steel	0.1% carbon	car bodies
stainless steel	1.5% carbon	ornamental railings

b) It's very brittle.

Q3 37.5% (9 ÷ 24 x 100 = 37.5)

Page 21 — Fractional Distillation of Crude Oil

Q1 a) Crude oil is a **mixture** of different molecules.

b) Most of the compounds in crude oil are **hydrocarbon** molecules.

c) The molecules in crude oil **aren't** chemically bonded to each other.

d) Physical methods **can** be used to separate out the molecules in crude oil.

Q2

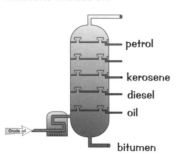

Q3 The larger the molecule the higher the boiling/condensing point.

Q4 The hydrocarbons all have different boiling points. During distillation the oil is heated and the different hydrocarbons boil off at different temperatures. The hydrocarbons can then be condensed individually and the crude oil is successfully separated.

Page 22 — Properties and Uses of Crude Oil

Q1 a)

methane   ethane   propane

b) propane

Q2 a) The longer the alkane molecule the **more** viscous (gloopy) it is

b) The shorter the alkane molecule the **lower** its boiling point.

c) The shorter the alkane molecule the **more** flammable it is.

Q3 a) C_nH_{2n+2}

b) $C_{20}H_{42}$ (n = 20 so 2n + 2 = (2 x 20) + 2 = 42)

Q4 a) Oils with long carbon chains are very viscous (gloopy) and so they cling to the moving parts of an engine, preventing damage.

b) Using a hydrocarbon with fewer carbon atoms would be problematic because it would vaporise when the engine got hot / could catch fire easily.

Page 23 — Using Crude Oil as a Fuel

Q1 a) The sun would not always be bright enough to work well / it wouldn't be possible to use solar power at night.

b) The wind wouldn't always be blowing when someone wanted to use the oven.

c) Nuclear substances would be very dangerous if they leaked / it would be very expensive to develop a way of storing the fuel in a safe way.

Q2 New reserves of oil have been discovered since the 1960s. Also, new methods of extraction mean that oil that was once too expensive or difficult to extract can now be used.

Q3 a) When oil is transported by ship there is the possibility of spills into the sea. Crude oil is poisonous to birds and sea creatures.

b) Burning oil products releases carbon dioxide, which causes global warming, and carbon particles (soot) which cause global dimming. The sulfur in oil will make sulfur dioxide which causes acid rain.

Chemistry 1a — Products from Rocks

Q4 Most technology around today is set up to use crude oil fractions as fuel and converting to alternatives would be time-consuming and costly. We need more energy than can currently be created using alternatives alone. Crude oil fractions are often more reliable than some alternatives, e.g. solar and wind power won't work without the right weather conditions.

Pages 24-25 — Environmental Problems

Q1 The main cause of acid rain is... sulfur dioxide.
Acid rain kills trees and... acidifies lakes.
Sulfur dioxide is produced by burning fuels which contain... sulfur.
Limestone buildings and statues are affected by... acid rain.
In clouds sulfur dioxide reacts with water to make... sulfuric acid.

Q2 Ways of reducing acid rain include:
Removing the sulfur from the fuel before it is burnt (using low-sulfur fuels).
Using scrubbers in power station chimneys to remove sulfur dioxide from emissions.

Q3 a) Carbon monoxide and carbon particles are formed when there is not enough oxygen for a hydrocarbon fuel to burn completely.
b) Carbon monoxide is poisonous.

Q4 a) i) false
ii) true
iii) true
iv) false
v) false
b) **Some** fuels produce carbon dioxide when burnt.
Oxides of nitrogen form if a fuel burns at **high** temperatures.
Soot forms if a fuel **undergoes partial combustion / Sulfur dioxide** forms if a fuel contains sulfur.

Q5 a) hydrocarbon + oxygen → carbon dioxide + water
b) i) Methane: $CH_4 + 2O_2 \rightarrow CO_2 + 2H_2O$
ii) Propane: $C_3H_8 + 5O_2 \rightarrow 3CO_2 + 4H_2O$

Q6 a) hydrocarbon + **oxygen** → water + carbon dioxide + **carbon monoxide + carbon**
b) Because carbon is produced in the form of soot.

Pages 26-29 — More Environmental Problems

Q1 a) The percentage of carbon dioxide in the atmosphere is increasing at an increasing (exponential) rate.
b) The burning of fossil fuels for energy.
c) It's causing the average temperature to increase.

Q2 Global dimming is the reduction in the amount of sunlight reaching the earth's surface. It's thought to be caused by particles of soot and ash produced when fossil fuels are burnt.

Q3 a) water
b) When hydrogen is used as a fuel no carbon dioxide is produced so it doesn't contribute to global warming. It doesn't produce particulates either. Also it doesn't produce sulfur dioxide so it doesn't cause acid rain.
c) Hydrogen-powered vehicles are very expensive because the engines they use are expensive. Hydrogen is difficult to store, which makes it awkward to use as a fuel. Fuelling stations would need to be adapted / converted.

Q4 a) water and carbon dioxide
b) Engines need to be converted before they'll work with ethanol fuels / ethanol fuel isn't widely available.

Q5 0.9 × 37 000 000 = 33 300 000 J or 33.3 MJ

Q6 a) Answers may include: walking/cycling instead of using vehicles, recycling metals, avoiding foods that have travelled a long way / buying locally produced food, saving electricity by turning lights off, not leaving electrical devices on stand-by, not flying (using other modes of transport that use less fossil fuels), etc.
b) Answer will depend on student's opinion — may argue that everyone who lives on Earth and uses its resources has a responsibility to try and prevent environmental damage. Alternatively, may suggest that new technologies will be able to prevent damage.

Q7 a) When burnt, biodiesel does produce carbon dioxide, but as it comes from recently grown plants which took in this carbon dioxide during their lives it does not increase the net level of the gas in the atmosphere.
b) Normal diesel is produced from crude oil, the remains of dead plants and animals from millions of years ago. When burnt it produces a net increase in the level of atmospheric carbon dioxide.

Q8 a) Recycled cooking oil
b) Climate change might slow down. Spills would be less harmful to the environment.
c) It has reduced the tax on biodiesel and increased the tax on normal diesel.
d) The Government would get less money from fuel tax. It would have to make cuts in other places (e.g. education) or raise the tax on something else.
e) E.g. you don't need to get a diesel car modified. Biodiesel may cost slightly more but the Government is actually making less money on it than it does on normal diesel.

Pages 30-33 — Mixed Questions — Chemistry 1a

Q1 a)

b) The following should be ticked:
Metals are generally strong but also malleable.
Metals conduct electricity well.
Properties of a metal can be altered by mixing it with another metal to form an alloy.
c) R. The material needs to be as light and as strong as possible with a high melting point and a reasonable price. S has a low melting point. T is expensive and fairly dense. U is not very strong and has a high density.

Q2 a) e.g. lubricants/bitumen for surfacing roads.
b) You could get oil spills, which damage the environment.

Q3 a) A finite resource is a resource of which there's a limited amount, which cannot be replenished.
b) i) In general, the more reactive the metal, the later it was discovered.
ii) Less reactive metals are easier to extract from their ores, for example by reduction with carbon. The least reactive metals are sometimes found uncombined in nature. The more reactive metals couldn't be extracted until electricity was discovered to do electrolysis.
c) i) iron(III) oxide + **carbon** → iron + **carbon dioxide**
ii) $2Fe_2O_3 + 3C \rightarrow 4Fe + 3CO_2$
d) i) Electrolysis produces very pure copper which conducts electricity better.
ii) Any two from: easily bent, easily drawn into wires, good conductor of electricity.
e) Aluminium is more reactive than carbon, and so cannot be extracted by reduction with carbon.

Chemistry 1b — Oils, Earth and Atmosphere

Q4 a) The following can be in any order:
Petrol has a lower melting and boiling point than diesel.
Petrol is more flammable (ignites more easily) than diesel.
Petrol is less viscous (flows more easily / is runnier) than diesel.
b) i) E.g. by the fermentation of sugar obtained from plants.
ii) When it's burnt, there are fewer pollutants than from petrol or diesel. / It's carbon neutral because it's made from plants.
Q5 a) Ace oil
b) The viscosity becomes much less.
c) Do the experiment at the average temperature of a car engine.
d) Duncan XYZ oil
Q6

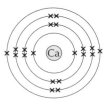

Q7 a) i)

ii) $CaCO_3 \rightarrow CaO + CO_2$
iii) E.g. neutralising acid soils in fields / acidity in lakes.
b)

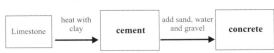

c) Any two of: it doesn't rot when it gets wet; it's cheaper; it's fire resistant; it can't be gnawed away by insects or rodents.
d) cement, sand and water
e) Acid rain reacts with the limestone and causes it to dissolve.

Chemistry 1b — Oils, Earth and Atmosphere

Page 34 — Cracking Crude Oil

Q1 shorter, petrol, diesel, long, high, catalyst, molecules, cracking
Q2 a) E.g. petrol, paraffin, ethene
b) thermal decomposition
Q3 a) ethene
b) 1. The long-chain molecules are heated.
2. They are vaporised (turned into a gas).
3. The vapour is passed over a catalyst at a high temperature.
4. The molecules are cracked on the surface of the catalyst.
Q4 a) kerosene → octane + ethene
b) $C_{10}H_{22} \rightarrow C_8H_{18} + C_2H_4$

Pages 35-36 — Alkenes and Ethanol

Q1 a) C_2H_4
b)

$$H\!\!\diagdown\!\!\underset{H}{\overset{}{C}}\!=\!\underset{H}{\overset{H}{C}}$$

c) Propene
d)

$$H\!\!\diagdown\!\!\underset{H}{\overset{}{C}}\!=\!\underset{H}{\overset{H}{C}}\!-\!\underset{H}{\overset{H}{C}}\!-\!H$$

Q2 a) C_5H_{10}
b) C_6H_{12}
c) C_8H_{16}
d) $C_{12}H_{24}$
Q3 a) False
b) True
c) False
d) True
Q4 bromine water, decolourise, bromine water, orange, colourless
Q5 a) A
b) Method A — Uses yeast.
Method B — Uses a catalyst.
c) Any two of:
Needs lower temperatures so is cheaper. Can use simpler equipment. Uses sugar which is often grown as a major crop. Sugar is a renewable resource.
d) The ethanol produced is not very concentrated/needs to be purified.
Q6 Ethene is a product of crude oil and crude oil is a non-renewable resource. When crude oil starts running out, using ethene to make ethanol will become very expensive.

Pages 37-38 — Using Alkenes to Make Polymers

Q1 The monomer of poly(ethene) is ethene.
Q2 Any three from:
e.g. plastic bags, waterproof coatings for fabrics, tooth fillings, hydrogel wound dressings, memory foam.
Q3 a) Waste remains in landfill. Landfill sites are getting full and more are needed, which takes up useful land.
b) Recycle and reuse.
c) Plastic is currently made from crude oil. As this runs low, its price will rise.
Q4

$$n\begin{pmatrix} CH_3 & H \\ | & | \\ C=C \\ | & | \\ H & H \end{pmatrix} \rightarrow \begin{pmatrix} CH_3 & H \\ | & | \\ C-C \\ | & | \\ H & H \end{pmatrix}_n$$

Q5 Polymers and cornstarch
Q6 Cracking is the breakdown of large molecules into smaller ones, whereas polymerisation is small molecules joining to form bigger molecules.
Cracking makes small alkenes and alkanes, polymerisation often uses alkenes to make alkanes.
Cracking usually involves breaking single bonds between carbon atoms. In polymerisation, the double bonds between carbon atoms are broken.

Pages 39-40 — Plant Oils

Q1 a) Fruits: e.g. avocados and olives
Seeds: e.g. brazil nuts and sesame seeds
b) e.g. food or fuel
c) It squeezes the oil out of the plant material.
Q2 Vegetable oils provide loads of energy, and also contain nutrients.
Q3 a) False
b) True
c) False
d) True
e) False
Q4 a) They provide lots of energy.
b) E.g. biodiesel
Q5 Martin has produced the better method. It is a fair test. He gives accurate quantities. He labels his equipment so there is less opportunity for mistakes.
Q6 a) Reaction with hydrogen with a nickel catalyst at about 60 °C. The double bonds open up and bond to the hydrogen atoms.
b) It increases the melting points of vegetable oils.

Chemistry 1b — Oils, Earth and Atmosphere

c) Some vegetable oils are only partially hydrogenated as turning all the double bonds into single bonds would make the oil too hard. Margarine is an example of this. It is partially hydrogenated so that it is spreadable.

Q7 a) saturated

b) They increase the amount of cholesterol in the blood, which can block arteries and lead to heart disease.

Page 41 — Emulsions

Q1 a) E.g. emulsions can be formed from oil suspended in water or water suspended in oil.

b) E.g. the thicker an emulsion, the more oil it contains.

c) E.g. emulsions can be combined with air and it makes them fluffier.

d) E.g. emulsions are found in foods as well as in non-food items such as moisturisers and paints.

Q2 a)

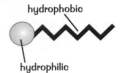

b) Lecithin molecules surround the droplets of oil, with their hydrophilic heads facing out into the water and their hydrophobic tails in the oil droplet. This layer keeps the oil droplets from joining together to separate out from the water.

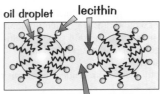

Q3 a) Emulsifiers increase the shelf-life of food by stopping emulsions from separating out.

b) Some people are allergic to certain emulsifiers, e.g. egg yolk, so they would need to check the ingredients very carefully.

Pages 42-43 — Plate Tectonics

Q1 continental drift, fossils, South America, Africa (alternative pairs of places are possible), land bridges, Pangaea, rotation.

Q2 False, True, True, False, True, False, False, False, True, True

Q3 Fossils of identical plants and animals were found on either side of the Atlantic.
The coastlines of South America and Africa seem to match.
Rocks with matching layers have been found on different continents.
Tropical plant fossils were found in the Arctic islands.

Q4 a) i) Tidal forces and the rotation of the Earth.

ii) The forces would have to be so great that they would stop the Earth from turning, which they hadn't/The forces he proposed were not strong enough.

iii) Any two from: He wasn't a qualified geologist. He had used flawed data. His idea just sounded so strange.

b) The ocean floors and mountains.

Pages 44-45 — The Earth's Structure

Q1 a) 1.6 × 10 000 = 16 000 cm = 0.16 km

b) 1.6 × 20 000 = 32 000 cm = 0.32 km
0.32 km + 325 km = 325.32 km

Q2 The main earthquake zones are along the plate boundaries.

Q3 A sphere showing 3 layers.
Labels: Crust (outer layer) — very thin, it varies between 5 km and 50 km thickness.
Mantle (next layer down) — properties of a solid but flows very slowly like a liquid. Radioactive decay takes place here.
Core (centre) — mostly iron and nickel.

Q4 Crust — Thinnest of the Earth's layers
Mantle — Slowly flowing semi-solid layer that plates float on
Convection current — Caused by heat from radioactive decay in the mantle
Tectonic plates — Large pieces of crust and upper mantle
Earthquakes — Caused by sudden movements of plates
Volcanoes — Hot spots that often sit on plate boundaries.

Q5 Earthquake: Evidence — Strain in underground rocks.
How reliable is it? — Can only suggest the possibility of an earthquake. Low reliability.
Volcanic eruption: Evidence — Rising molten rock causing the ground to bulge slightly, leading to mini-earthquakes.
How reliable is it? — Molten rock can cool instead of erupting, so not a definite sign. Low/medium reliability.

Pages 46-47 — The Evolution of the Atmosphere

Q1 a) True
b) False
c) True

Q2 The percentage of carbon dioxide has decreased by a large amount because it dissolved into the oceans and a lot of it was converted into limestone from the shells of marine organisms. Plants also used carbon dioxide in the air for photosynthesis.

Q3 The statements should be in this order (from the top of the timeline):
1. The atmosphere is about four-fifths nitrogen and one-fifth oxygen.
2. The build-up of oxygen in the atmosphere allows more complex organisms to evolve and flourish.
The oxygen also creates the ozone layer.
3. Green plants and algae evolve over most of the Earth. They're quite happy in the CO_2 atmosphere. A lot of the CO_2 dissolves into the oceans. The green plants and algae also absorb some of the CO_2 and produce O_2 by photosynthesis.
4. Water vapour condenses to form oceans.
5. The Earth cools down slightly. A thin crust forms. There's lots of volcanic activity.
6. The Earth's surface is molten — it's so hot that any atmosphere just 'boils away' into space.

Q4 a) Largest sector is Nitrogen, second largest is Oxygen, smallest is Carbon dioxide and other gases.

b) Nitrogen: 80% approx (to be more precise, it's 78% in dry air)
Oxygen: 20% approx (to be more precise, it's 21% in dry air)

c) Nitrogen has increased. Carbon dioxide has decreased. Far less water vapour now. Oxygen is now a significant proportion of the atmosphere.

d) As the planet cooled, the water vapour condensed and formed the oceans.

e) Plants and algae photosynthesised and produced it.

f) In any order:
Created the ozone layer which blocked harmful rays from the Sun.
Killed off early organisms/allowed more complex ones to evolve.

Chemistry 2a — Bonding and Calculations

Pages 48-49 — Life, Resources and Atmospheric Change

Q1 a)
1. Air is filtered to remove dust.
2. Air is cooled to -200 °C.
3. Carbon dioxide freezes and is removed. Water vapour condenses and is removed.
4. Liquefied air enters the fractionating column and is heated slowly.
  b) mixture, boiling points
  c) E.g. oxygen, nitrogen.

Q2 a) Billions of years ago, the earth's atmosphere was mainly nitrogen, hydrogen, ammonia and methane. Lightning struck causing a chemical reaction between these gases and as a result amino acids were formed. The amino acids collected in a 'primordial soup' — a body of water out of which life gradually crawled.
  b) Miller and Urey sealed the gases, nitrogen, hydrogen, ammonia and methane in some apparatus, heated them and applied an electrical charge for a week.
  c) Amino acids were created, but not as many as there are on Earth. This suggests that the theory is along the right lines but perhaps not quite right.

Q3 a) Burning fossil fuels
  b) i) Generally increased, although it has fluctuated.
    ii) Global warming

Q4 As the level of CO_2 rises, the amount of CO_2 that the oceans absorb is also rising. The oceans are a natural store of CO_2 but all the extra CO_2 that they are absorbing is making them too acidic. This is causing shellfish and coral to die.

Pages 50-52 — Mixed Questions — Chemistry 1b

Q1 a) There are twice as many hydrogen atoms as there are carbon atoms in each molecule (and no other atoms).
  b)
$$H-\overset{\overset{\displaystyle H}{|}}{\underset{\underset{\displaystyle H}{|}}{C}}-\overset{\overset{\displaystyle H}{|}}{C}=C\overset{\diagup H}{\diagdown H}$$
  c) Alkanes only have single bonds, alkenes have a double bond between some carbon atoms. (The general formula of an alkane is C_nH_{2n+2}.)

Q2 a) cracking
  b) Ethene can be hydrated with steam to produce ethanol. This requires a high temperature, high pressure and a catalyst.
  c) Ethanol can be made by fermentation of sugar. Sugar is obtained from plants which are renewable.

Q3 a) Lots of small molecules (monomers) join up to make long chain molecules (polymers).
  b) Name: polystyrene / poly(styrene)
  c) E.g. it's difficult to get rid of them / they fill up landfill sites.

Q4 a) Any one from:
By crushing rapeseed and then pressing it to extract the oil. / By crushing rapeseed and then using a centrifuge. / By crushing rapeseed and then using a solvent.
  b) Rapeseed oil will turn bromine water from orange to colourless.
  c) E.g. heart disease.
  d) i) An emulsifier stops the oil and water in an emulsion from separating out.
    ii) Advantage: Longer shelf life / the food is lower in fat but still has a good texture.
Disadvantage: some people are allergic to some emulsifiers e.g. egg yolk.

Q5 a) E.g. the changes which provided evidence happen very slowly. Technological advances have only recently made it possible to investigate things like the ocean floor.
  b) Convection currents in the mantle.
  c) Earthquakes and volcanoes

Q6 a) No. It would not support animal life because there is no oxygen. It could support plant life because there is plenty of carbon dioxide for photosynthesis.
  b) i) Green plants and algae.
    ii) The oceans absorbed CO_2.
  c) i) increasing, carbon dioxide, burning
    ii) Any one from:
global warming / climate change.
  d) i) False, only 1% of the atmosphere is noble gases.
    ii) True
    iii) False, scientists can't predict volcanoes and earthquakes with any accuracy.

Chemistry 2a — Bonding and Calculations

Page 53 — Atoms, Compounds and Isotopes

Q1

Particle	Mass
Proton	1
Neutron	1
Electron	0

Q2 a)

  b) The total number of protons and neutrons in an atom.
  c) compound

Q3 Isotopes, element, protons, neutrons.

Q4 W and Y, because these two atoms have the same number of protons but a different mass number.

Pages 54-55 — Ionic Bonding

Q1 a) i) true
    ii) true
    iii) false
    iv) true
    v) false
    vi) true
  b) iii) E.g. atoms form ionic bonds to give them the same electronic structure as the noble gases.
    v) E.g. in ionic bonding, electrons from the outer shell are transferred.

Q2 a) 2
  b) 2

Q3 a) strong, positive, negative, all directions, large
  b) Any two from: e.g. high boiling point / will dissolve to form solutions that conduct electricity / will conduct electricity when molten

Q4 a) i) should be ticked
  b) Sodium chloride has a cuboid shape because the electrostatic forces of attraction hold the oppositely charged ions together in a regular lattice arrangement.

Chemistry 2a — Bonding and Calculations

Q5 a)

	Conducts electricity?
When solid	No
When dissolved in water	Yes
When molten	Yes

b) When solid, the ions are held tightly in a giant ionic lattice so they're unable to move and conduct electricity. When dissolved or molten, the ions are free to move and so can conduct electricity.

Page 56 — Ions and Formulas

Q1 a) Group 1
b) 1
c) 1^+
d) NaCl
Q2 non-metals, 1^+ charge, negative, 1^- charge
Q3 BeS, K_2S, BeI_2, KI
Q4 a) KBr
b) $FeCl_2$
c) CaF_2

Page 57 — Electronic Structure of Ions

Q1 a)

b)

c)

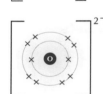

Q2 a) $CaCl_2$
b)

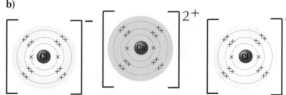

Pages 58-59 — Covalent Bonding

Q1 a) true
b) true
c) true
d) false
e) true
Q2

Atom	Carbon	Chlorine	Hydrogen	Nitrogen	Oxygen
Number of electrons needed to fill outer shell	4	1	1	3	2

Q3 Both atoms need to gain electrons. Sharing electrons allows both atoms to achieve the stable 'full outer shell' of electrons.

Q4 a)

b)

c)

Q5 a)

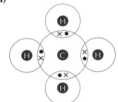

b)

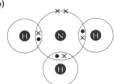

Q6 a) Atoms only share electrons in their outer energy levels/ shells.
b) 1.

Cl — Cl

2.

$\times\times$ $\bullet\bullet$

$\times\times$ Cl $\times\bullet$ Cl $\bullet\vdots$

$\times\times$ $\bullet\bullet$

Pages 60-61 — Covalent Substances: Two Kinds

Q1 Diamond — I am used in drill tips; I am the hardest natural substance; My carbon atoms form four covalent bonds.
Graphite — I have layers which move over one another; I am used in pencils; I am a good conductor of electricity; My carbon atoms form three covalent bonds.
Silicon dioxide — I am also known as silica; I am not made from carbon.
Q2 atoms, strong, high
Q3 a) Any two from: e.g. low melting point / low boiling point / doesn't conduct electricity
b) E.g. it has weak intermolecular forces so its molecules are easily parted from each other. / There are no ions so there's no electrical charge. / There are no ions to carry the current.
Q4 a) simple molecular and giant covalent/macromolecules
b) i) silicon dioxide
ii) graphite
iii) diamond

c) Any two from: e.g. it has a very high melting point. / It has a very high boiling point. / It doesn't conduct electricity.
Q5 a) i) Each carbon atom in graphite has one delocalised (free) electron. These free electrons conduct electricity.
ii) Graphite is made up of layers which are free to slide over each other. There are only weak intermolecular forces between the layers, so graphite is soft and slippery.
b) Each carbon atom forms four covalent bonds in a very rigid giant covalent structure.

Pages 62-63 — Metallic Structures

Q1 a) giant
b) heat
c) atoms
Q2 a) electrons, outer, strong, positive, regular
b) They have delocalised electrons which are free to move through the whole structure and conduct electricity.
Q3 a) An alloy is a mixture of two or more metals.
b) In pure metals the regular layers of atoms are able to slide over each other. This means they can be bent. However, in alloys there are atoms of more than one size. This distorts the layers and prevents them from being able to slide over each other. This makes brass harder than copper.
Q4 a) giant ionic
b) giant covalent
c) giant metallic
Q5

Property	Giant Ionic	Giant Covalent	Simple Molecular	Giant Metallic
High melting and boiling points	✓	✓	✗	✓
Can conduct electricity when solid	✗	✗ except graphite	✗	✓
Can conduct electricity when molten	✓	✗ except graphite	✗	✓

Q6 a) giant ionic — it only conducts electricity when molten or dissolved.
b) giant covalent — high melting point, but doesn't conduct electricity.
c) simple molecular — low melting point.
d) giant metallic — conducts electricity.

Pages 64-65 — New Materials

Q1 a) i) true
ii) false
iii) true
b) E.g. nitinol is affected by temperature.
c) It remembers its original shape — so if you bend it out of shape, you can heat it and it goes back to its 'remembered' shape.
d) E.g. dental braces / glasses frames
Q2 a) hundred, different
b) They have a huge surface area to volume ratio.
Q3 $1 \div 0.000\ 001 = \mathbf{1\ 000\ 000\ nm}$
Q4 a) fullerenes, molecules, hexagonal, atoms
b) Lightweight but strong — Building materials
Can detect specific molecules — Sensors to test water purity
Act like ball bearings to reduce friction — Lubricants for artificial joints
c) nanoscience
d) They are so small that they are absorbed more easily by the body than most particles.
Q5 a) They can conduct electricity.
b) The carbon atoms in nanotubes are joined by covalent bonds which makes them very strong.

Page 66 — Polymers

Q1 a) A
b) Thermosetting polymers have strong intermolecular forces called crosslinks between the polymer chains.
Q2 What the starting materials are and what the reaction conditions are.
Q3 a) LDP — toothpaste tubes need to be flexible so you can squeeze the paste out.
b) LDP — freezer bags also need to be flexible.
c) HDP — The equipment needs to have a high softening temperature so it can be sterilised by heating.

Page 67 — Relative Formula Mass

Q1 a) How heavy an atom of an element is compared to an atom of carbon-12.
b) i) 24
ii) 20
iii) 16
iv) 1
v) 12
vi) 63.5
vii) 39
viii) 40
ix) 35.5
Q2 Element A is helium
Element B is $(3 \times 4) = 12$ = carbon
Element C is $(4 \times 4) = 16$ = oxygen
Q3 a) You add the A_r of all the atoms in the compound together.
b) i) $(2 \times 1) + 16 = 18$
ii) $39 + 16 + 1 = 56$
iii) $1 + 14 + (3 \times 16) = 63$
iv) $(2 \times 1) + 32 + (4 \times 16) = 98$
v) $14 + (4 \times 1) + 14 + (3 \times 16) = 80$
Q4 $2XOH + H_2 = 114$
$2 \times (X + 16 + 1) + (2 \times 1) = 114$
$2 \times (X + 17) + 2 = 114$
$2 \times (X + 17) = 112$
$X + 17 = 56$
$X = 39$
so X = potassium

Page 68 — Two Formula Mass Calculations

Q1 a) Percentage mass of an element in a compound =
$$\frac{A_r \times \text{No. of atoms (of that element)}}{M_r \text{ (of whole compound)}} \times 100$$
b) i) $(14 \times 2) \div [14 + (4 \times 1) + 14 + (3 \times 16)] \times 100 = 35\%$
ii) $(4 \times 1) \div [14 + (4 \times 1) + 14 + (3 \times 16)] \times 100 = 5\%$
iii) $(3 \times 16) \div [14 + (4 \times 1) + 14 + (3 \times 16)] \times 100 = 60\%$
Q2 a) A = $(3 \times 16) \div [(2 \times 56) + (3 \times 16)] \times 100 = 30\%$
B = $16 \div [(2 \times 1) + 16] \times 100 = 89\%$
C = $(3 \times 16) \div [40 + 12 + (3 \times 16)] \times 100 = 48\%$
b) B
Q3 a) $14 \div (14 + 16) \times 100 = 47\%$
b)

	Nitrogen	Oxygen
Percentage mass (%)	30.4	69.6
$\div A_r$	$(30.4 \div 14) = 2.17$	$(69.6 \div 16) = 4.35$
Ratio	1	2

empirical formula = NO_2

Q4

	Calcium	Oxygen	Hydrogen
Mass (g)	0.8	0.64	0.04
$\div A_r$	$(0.8 \div 40) = 0.02$	$(0.64 \div 16) = 0.04$	$(0.04 \div 1) = 0.04$
Ratio	1	2	2

empirical formula = $Ca(OH)_2$ (or CaO_2H_2)

Chemistry 2a — Bonding and Calculations

Pages 69-70 — Calculating Masses in Reactions

Q1 a) $2Mg + O_2 \rightarrow 2MgO$

b)

2Mg	2MgO
$2 \times 24 = 48$	$2 \times (24 + 16) = 80$
$48 \div 48 = 1$ g	$80 \div 48 = 1.67$ g
$1 \times 10 = 10$ g	$1.67 \times 10 = \textbf{16.7 g}$

Q2

4Na	$2Na_2O$
$4 \times 23 = 92$	$2 \times [(2 \times 23) + 16] = 124$
$92 \div 124 = 0.74$ g	$124 \div 124 = 1$ g
$0.74 \times 2 = \textbf{1.5 g}$	$1 \times 2 = 2$ g

Q3 a) $2Al + Fe_2O_3 \rightarrow Al_2O_3 + 2Fe$

b)

Fe_2O_3	2Fe
$[(2 \times 56) + (3 \times 16)] = 160$	$2 \times 56 = 112$
$160 \div 160 = 1$ g	$112 \div 160 = 0.7$
$1 \times 20 = 20$ g	$0.7 \times 20 = \textbf{14 g}$

Q4 $CaCO_3 \rightarrow CaO + CO_2$

$CaCO_3$	CaO
$40 + 12 + (3 \times 16) = 100$	$40 + 16 = 56$
$100 \div 56 = 1.786$ kg	$56 \div 56 = 1$ kg
$1.786 \times 100 = \textbf{178.6 kg}$	$1 \times 100 = 100$ kg

Q5 a)

C	2CO
12	$2 \times (12 + 16) = 56$
$12 \div 12 = 1$ g	$56 \div 12 = 4.67$ g
$1 \times 10 = 10$ g	$4.67 \times 10 = 46.7$ g

46.7 g of CO is produced in stage B — all this is used in stage C.

3CO	$3CO_2$
$3 \times (12 + 16) = 84$	$3 \times [12 + (2 \times 16)] = 132$
$84 \div 84 = 1$ g	$132 \div 84 = 1.57$ g
$1 \times 46.7 = 46.7$ g	$1.57 \times 46.7 = \textbf{73.3 g}$

b) It could be recycled and used in stage B.

Q6 a) $2NaOH + H_2SO_4 \rightarrow Na_2SO_4 + 2H_2O$

b)

2NaOH	Na_2SO_4
$2 \times (23 + 16 + 1) = 80$	$(2 \times 23) + 32 + (4 \times 16) = 142$
$80 \div 142 = 0.56$ g	$142 \div 142 = 1$ g
$0.56 \times 75 = \textbf{42 g}$	$1 \times 75 = 75$ g

c)

H_2SO_4	$2H_2O$
$(2 \times 1) + 32 + (4 \times 16) = 98$	$2 \times [(2 \times 1) + 16] = 36$
$98 \div 98 = 1$ g	$36 \div 98 = 0.37$ g
$1 \times 50 = 50$ g	$0.37 \times 50 = \textbf{18.5 g}$

Page 71 — Percentage Yield and Reversible Reactions

Q1 a) yield, higher, percentage yield, predicted

b) $(6 \div 15) \times 100 = 40\%$

c) When the solution was filtered a bit of barium sulfate may have been lost. Less product means a lower percentage yield.

d) i) Not all the reactants are turned into products because the reaction goes both ways. So the percentage yield is reduced.

ii) The unexpected reaction will use up the reactants, so there's not as much left to make the product you want. So the percentage yield is reduced.

Q2 E.g. a low yield means wasted chemicals which isn't sustainable. Increasing the yield would save resources for the future.

Page 72 — Chemical Analysis and Instrumental Methods

Q1 a) Extract the colour from the sweet by placing it in a small cup with a few drops of solvent. Put a spot of the coloured solution on a pencil baseline on filter paper. Put the paper in a beaker of solvent (keep the baseline above the solvent). After the solvent has seeped up the paper, measure the distance the dyes have travelled. Repeat for each sweet.

b) Blue has 2 dyes.

c) Brown, because the same pattern of dyes are present.

Q2 a) E.g. they're very fast

b) E.g. they're very accurate and very sensitive/can detect even the tiniest amounts of a substance.

Q3 a) i) 2

ii) 6 and 10 minutes

b) Work out the relative molecular mass of each of the substances from the graph it draws.

Pages 73-75 — Mixed Questions — Chemistry 2a

Q1 a) i) giant covalent

ii) All the atoms are bonded to each other by strong covalent bonds so it takes a lot of energy to separate the carbon atoms.

b) i) T

ii) nanoparticle / fullerene

Q2 a)

	Silicon	Chlorine
Mass (g)	1.4	7.1
$\div A_r$	$(1.4 \div 28) = 0.05$	$(7.1 \div 35.5) = 0.2$
Ratio	1	4

Empirical formula = $SiCl_4$

b) $(35.5 \times 4) \div [(35.5 \times 4) + 28] \times 100 = \textbf{83.5\%}$

c) $Si + 2Cl_2 \rightarrow SiCl_4$

d)

Si	$SiCl_4$
28	$28 + (4 \times 35.5) = 170$
$28 \div 28 = 1$ g	$170 \div 28 = 6.07$ g
$1 \times 1.4 = 1.4$ g	$6.07 \times 1.4 = \textbf{8.5 g}$

Q3 a) Any one from: A / B / F.
Simple molecular substances have weak intermolecular forces and therefore low melting and boiling points. / They do not conduct electricity since there are no ions and so no charge.

b) C

c) All metals are good conductors of electricity when solid. / Substance D is a poor conductor of electricity when solid.

Q4 a) false

b) false

c) true

Q5 a) $24 + [2 \times (14 + 16 \times 3)] = 148$

b)

Mg	$Mg(NO_3)_2$
24	$24 + [2 \times (14 + 16 \times 3)] = 148$
$24 \div 24 = 1$ g	$148 \div 24 = 6.17$ g
$1 \times 12 = 12$ g	$6.17 \times 12 = \textbf{74 g}$

c) E.g. in a reversible reaction some of the products turn back into the reactants. / Unexpected reactions can take place and use up some of the reactants. / Some liquid or solid can be lost during filtration.

Q6 a) i) ionic compound

ii) metal

iii) alloy

b) i) substance i) (ionic compound)

ii) Ionic substances don't conduct electricity when solid as the ions are not free to move.

c) $CaCl_2$

Chemistry 2b — Reaction Rates, Salts and Electrolysis

Q7 a) gas, speeds, chromatograph, compounds, retention time, identify, mass spectrometer

b) E.g. it's more accurate.

Chemistry 2b — Reaction Rates, Salts and Electrolysis

Page 76 — Rate of Reaction

Q1 a) higher

b) lower

c) decreases

d) does

Q2 a) i) Z

ii) It has the steepest gradient. / It becomes flat sooner.

b) Equal masses of marble chips were used each time.

c) The curve should be steeper and show that a larger volume of gas is produced, e.g. like this:

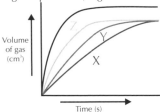

Q3 a) decrease

b) More reactant was used.

c) The reactants in Q might be in smaller pieces/have a larger surface area/be more concentrated/be at a higher temperature.

Pages 77-78 — Measuring Rates of Reaction

Q1 rate, reactants, formed, precipitation, faster, gas, mass, volume

Q2 a) C

b) i) Point K: $0.08 \div 5 = 0.016$ g/s

ii) Point L: $0.06 \div 15 = 0.004$ g/s

Q3 a)

Average volume of gas produced (cm^3)
94
64
45.5
35
9

b) 50 in the third column of the table should be circled.

c) 2 mol/dm^3

d) i) gas syringe

ii) Any one from: e.g. stopwatch / stopclock / timer / balance / measuring cylinder

e) Sketch should look something like this:

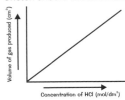

f) To improve the reliability of his results.

g) E.g. misreading the value from the gas syringe. / Not emptying the gas syringe before starting.

Pages 79-82 — Rate of Reaction Experiments

Q1 increase, faster, smaller, react

Q2 a) B

b) Curve should look something like this:

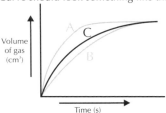

c) Size of marble pieces.

d) No, you cannot tell if it was a fair test. The same mass of marble chips was used each time but it is not known if the same volume of HCl was used each time or if the temperature was kept constant.

e) Measuring how quickly the reaction loses mass.

Q3 a) 13 (he took one at the start).

b) x-axis: time (s)
y-axis: change/loss in mass (g)

c)

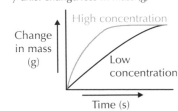

d) $145.73 - 143.89 = 1.84$ g

Q4 a) 1, because the slope of the graph is steepest.

b)

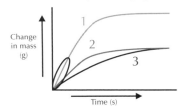

c) The reactions finish eventually. / The reactants are always used up eventually.

Q5 The mixture goes cloudy.

Q6 a) water bath, stopclock, thermometer.

b) i) faster

ii) 145 s

c) i) temperature

ii) time taken for cross to disappear

d) Repeat the investigation to get more results and find the average for each temperature.

Q7 Increasing the concentration of HCl increases the rate of reaction.

Q8 a) $2H_2O$

b) C

c) increase

Q9 a) Volume of gas (cm^3/dm^3/l/ml)

b) i) R

ii) Reaction R has the steepest graph and becomes flat sooner, so it is the fastest reaction and must have the most effective catalyst.

Chemistry 2b — Reaction Rates, Salts and Electrolysis

Page 83 — Collision Theory

Q1 increasing the temperature — makes the particles move faster, so they collide more often
decreasing the concentration — means fewer particles of reactant are present, so less frequent collisions occur
increasing the surface area — gives particles a bigger area of solid reactant to react with

Q2 a) energy
b) faster, more
c) rate of reaction
Q3 a) i) increase
ii) The particles are closer together so collisions happen more frequently.
b)

low pressure   high pressure

Q4 a) false
b) true
c) false
d) true

Page 84 — Collision Theory and Catalysts

Q1 Activation energy is the minimum amount of energy needed by particles to react.
Q2 a) A catalyst is a substance which speeds up a reaction, without being changed or used up in the reaction.
b) i) A
ii) Reaction A has the steepest graph and becomes flat sooner so it's the fastest reaction. This means it must have used a catalyst.
Q3 a) Any one from: e.g. they allow the reaction to take place at a much lower temperature. This reduces the energy used which saves money. / They increase the rate of the reaction, so costs are reduced because the plant doesn't have to operate for as long.
b) Any two from: e.g. they can be expensive to buy. / A plant making more than one product will need more than one catalyst. / They can be poisoned by impurities and stop working.
c) E.g. the Haber process uses an iron catalyst.

Pages 85-86 — Energy Transfer in Reactions

Q1 to, heat, rise, temperature
Q2 a) N, B
b) combustion
c) E.g. adding sodium to water.
Q3 take in, heat, fall/decrease
Q4 a) thermal decomposition
b) i) endothermic
ii) The reaction takes in heat from the surroundings.
c) i) $1\,800\,000 \div 1000 = 1800$ kJ
ii) $90\,000 \div 1\,800\,000 = 0.05$ tonnes or 50 kg
Q5 a) When he dropped water on it. / When it turned blue. / The second part.
b) When he heated up the copper sulphate. / The first part. / When it went white.
c) hydrated.
d) hydrated copper sulfate $\rightleftharpoons$ anhydrous copper sulfate + water
e) reversible reaction

Q6 a) X
b) N
c) X
d) N

Pages 87-88 — Acids and Alkalis

Q1 a) acid + base $\rightarrow$ **salt + water**
b) neutralisation
c) i) $H^+_{(aq)}$ and $OH^-_{(aq)}$
ii) $H^+_{(aq)}$
iii) $OH^-_{(aq)}$
iv) $OH^-_{(aq)}$
v) $H^+_{(aq)}$
Q2 a) neutral
b) E.g. universal indicator
c) 7
d) alkali
Q3 a) $HCl_{(aq)} + NaOH_{(aq)} \rightarrow \textbf{NaCl}_{(aq)} + \textbf{H}_2\textbf{O}_{(l)}$
b) $H^+_{(aq)} + OH^-_{(aq)} \rightarrow H_2O_{(l)}$
c) an indicator (e.g. Universal indicator)
d) pH 7
Q4 a) s
b) l
c) g
d) aq
Q5 a) baking soda or soap powder
b) They are weak bases and so would neutralise the acid but wouldn't irritate or harm the skin. (Stronger bases like caustic soda might damage the skin).
Q6 a)

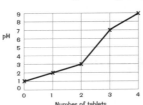

b) The pH increases from pH 1 to pH 9. (It increases most sharply between pH 3 and pH 7).
c) 3

Pages 89-90 — Acids Reacting with Metals

Q1 a)

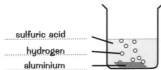

sulfuric acid
hydrogen
aluminium

b) aluminium + **sulfuric acid** $\rightarrow$ aluminium sulfate + **hydrogen**
c) $2Al + 3H_2SO_4 \rightarrow Al_2(SO_4)_3 + 3H_2$
d) zinc + sulfuric acid $\rightarrow$ zinc sulfate + hydrogen
e) $Mg + 2HCl \rightarrow MgCl_2 + H_2$
Q2 a) A
b) B
c) A: magnesium
B: copper
C: iron
D: zinc
Q3 a) E.g. the number of gas bubbles produced in a certain time. / The time it takes for the metal to disappear completely. / The volume of gas produced in a certain time. / Loss of mass in a certain time.
b) acid concentration
c) Any two from: e.g. volume of acid. / Mass of the metal pieces. / Size of the metal pieces. / Temperature.

Q4 metals, hydrogen, copper, reactive, more, chloride, sulfuric, nitric
Q5 a) i) $Ca + 2HCl \rightarrow CaCl_2 + H_2$
ii) $2Na + 2HCl \rightarrow 2NaCl + H_2$
iii) $2Li + H_2SO_4 \rightarrow Li_2SO_4 + H_2$
b) i) magnesium bromide
ii) $2Al + 6HBr \rightarrow 2AlBr_3 + 3H_2$

Pages 91-92 — Oxides, Hydroxides and Ammonia

Q1 a) hydrochloric acid + lead oxide $\rightarrow$ **lead** chloride + water
b) nitric acid + copper hydroxide $\rightarrow$ copper **nitrate** + water
c) sulfuric acid + zinc oxide $\rightarrow$ zinc sulfate + **water**
d) hydrochloric acid + **nickel** oxide $\rightarrow$ nickel **chloride** + **water**
e) **nitric** acid + copper oxide $\rightarrow$ **copper** nitrate + **water**
f) sulfuric acid + **sodium** hydroxide $\rightarrow$ sodium **sulfate** + **water**
Q2 a) The following should be ticked:
Acids react with metal oxides to form a salt and water.
Salts and water are formed when acids react with metal hydroxides.
Ammonia solution is alkaline.
b) $H_2SO_4 + CuO \rightarrow CuSO_4 + H_2O$
$HCl + NaOH \rightarrow NaCl + H_2O$
Q3 a) E.g. potassium oxide/hydroxide + sulfuric acid
b) ammonia + hydrochloric acid
c) E.g. silver oxide/hydroxide + nitric acid
Q4 a) NH_3
b) alkaline, nitrogen, proteins, salts, fertilisers
c) ammonia + nitric acid $\rightarrow$ ammonium nitrate
d) Because it has nitrogen from two sources, the ammonia and the nitric acid.
e) No water is produced.
Q5 a) i) $CuO_{(s)}$
ii) $H_2O_{(l)}$
iii) $HCl_{(aq)}$
iv) $ZnO_{(s)}$
v) $Na_2SO_{4(aq)} + 2H_2O_{(l)}$
b) i) $2NaOH + H_2SO_4 \rightarrow Na_2SO_4 + 2H_2O$
ii) $Mg(OH)_2 + 2HNO_3 \rightarrow Mg(NO_3)_2 + 2H_2O$
iii) $2NH_3 + H_2SO_4 \rightarrow (NH_4)_2SO_4$

Pages 93-94 — Making Salts

Q1 a) soluble
b) insoluble
c) acids, neutralised
d) precipitation
Q2 a) B
b) C
c) A
Q3 a) **silver nitrate + sodium chloride** $\rightarrow$ silver chloride + **sodium nitrate**
b) The silver chloride must be filtered out of the solution. It needs to be washed and then dried on filter paper.
c) E.g. the removal of poisonous ions from drinking water. / The removal of calcium and magnesium ions from hard water.
Q4 a) The nickel oxide will sink to the bottom of the flask.
b) i)

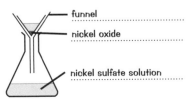

funnel
nickel oxide
nickel sulfate solution

ii) filtration

c) Evaporate some of the water (to make the solution more concentrated) and then leave the rest to evaporate very slowly.
d) nickel and nickel hydroxide
e) i) As potassium hydroxide is a soluble base, you can't tell when the reaction is finished — you can't just add an excess of solid to the acid and filter out what's left.
ii) You have to add exactly the right amount of alkali to just neutralise the acid — you need to use an indicator to show when the reaction's finished. Then repeat using exactly the same volumes of alkali and acid so the salt isn't contaminated with indicator.

Page 95 — Electrolysis

Q1 electric current, ionic, molten, elements, electrolysis, liquid, free ions, conduct, flow, positive, negative, atoms/molecules, molecules/atoms
Q2 a) It could be melted.
b) lead and bromine
c) i) true
ii) false
iii) true
iv) false
v) false

Page 96 — Electrolysis of Sodium Chloride Solution

Q1 a) The product is hydrogen unless the metal ions are less reactive than hydrogen — in which case the metal ions will form atoms.
b) hydrogen
Q2 sodium chloride, chlorine, plastics/bleach, bleach/plastics, negative electrode, sodium hydroxide, soap
Q3 a) A: H^+
B: Cl^-
C: H_2
D: Cl_2
b) Positive electrode: $2Cl^- \rightarrow Cl_2 + 2e^-$
Negative electrode: $2H^+ + 2e^- \rightarrow H_2$

Page 97 — Extraction of Aluminium and Electroplating

Q1 a) i) bauxite
ii) aluminium oxide, Al_2O_3
b) i) false
ii) true
iii) true
iv) false
v) false
c) The oxygen produced at the positive electrode reacts with the carbon in the electrode to produce carbon dioxide. So the positive electrodes gradually get 'eaten away'.
Q2 a)

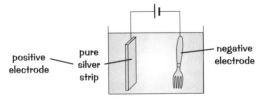

positive electrode — pure silver strip — negative electrode

b) silver/Ag^+
c) E.g. to make it look attractive without the expense of making it from solid silver.
d) E.g. plating metals for electronic circuits / computers.

Chemistry 3a — Elements, Water and Organic Chemistry

Pages 98-100 — Mixed Questions — Chemistry 2b

Q1 a) Increasing the temperature.
Increasing the concentration of the reactants (or the pressure if it's a gas).
Adding a catalyst.
Increasing the surface area of solid reactants.
b) The amount of product formed.
Q2 a) Q
b) R
c) Measure the volume of gas given off using a gas syringe.
Q3 a) true
b) true
c) false
d) true
e) true
Q4 a) i) acidic
ii) alkaline
b) i) neutralisation
ii) exothermic
Q5 a) $Mg + 2HCl \rightarrow MgCl_2 + H_2$
b) The pH would increase. / It would become less acidic, until it finally reached neutral/pH 7 (if there was enough magnesium).
c) Magnesium sulfate.
Q6 a) i) They gain electrons to become aluminium atoms again.
ii) $Al^{3+}_{(aq)} + 3e^- \rightarrow Al_{(s)}$
b) $2O^{2-}_{(aq)} \rightarrow O_{2(g)} + 4e^-$
Q7 Aluminium oxide has a very high melting point. Dissolving it in molten cryolite brings the melting point down. This reduces the energy needed and makes the electrolysis cheaper.
Q8 a) i) $MgCl_2$
ii) $MgO_{(s)} + 2HCl_{(aq)} \rightarrow MgCl_{2(aq)} + H_2O_{(l)}$
b) sulfuric acid/H_2SO_4
c) bases
Q9 a) i) hydrogen and chlorine
ii) E.g. chlorine is used in the manufacture of plastics. / Chlorine is used in the manufacture of bleach.
b) The sodium ions stay in solution because they're more reactive than hydrogen. Hydroxide ions from water are also left behind. This means that sodium hydroxide (NaOH) is left in the solution.
c) Coating the surface of one metal with another metal.

Chemistry 3a — Elements, Water and Organic Chemistry

Page 101 — History of the Periodic Table

Q1 a) atomic number
b) atomic mass
Q2 a) true
b) false
c) true
d) false
Q3 a) germanium, 5.32 g/cm³
b) i) E.g. they both arranged the elements in order of atomic mass. / They both arranged elements with similar properties into groups.
ii) Unlike Newlands, Mendeleev left gaps for undiscovered elements.
iii) Any one from: e.g. he didn't leave gaps for undiscovered elements. / His groups contained elements with different properties. / His groups mixed up metals and non-metals.
Q4 When elements are arranged in order of atomic mass, a periodic pattern in their properties can be seen.

Pages 102-103 — The Modern Periodic Table

Q1 fun, predicting, properties, discovered, atomic number, chemical
Q2 a) K
b) Li
c) K
Q3 a) The number of outer electrons is the same as the group number.
b) magnesium = 2, 8, 2
oxygen = 2, 6
sulfur = 2, 8, 6
c) Fluorine is more reactive than chlorine because its outer shell of electrons is closer to the nucleus, so it attracts electrons more strongly.
Q4 a) i) The outer electrons are further from the nucleus and so aren't attracted to the nucleus as strongly.
ii) more reactive
b) i) Fluorine's outermost shell is closer to the nucleus than bromine's so the attraction is greater.
ii) The reactivity decreases down the group because the attraction for electrons decreases.
Q5 a) Group 1
b) These elements would be less reactive. As you go down a group, elements contain more shells of electrons, so there's an increased distance from the nucleus. The outer electron's more easily lost.

Page 104 — Group 1 — The Alkali Metals

Q1 a) false
b) false
c) true
d) true
e) false
Q2 sodium hydroxide, hydrogen, electron, positive
Q3 The metals get more reactive further down the group because the outer electron is more easily lost as it's further from the nucleus.
Q4 a) Lithium is less dense than water.
b) alkaline
c) i) lithium + water → lithium hydroxide + hydrogen
ii) $2Li_{(s)} + 2H_2O_{(l)} \rightarrow 2LiOH_{(aq)} + H_{2(g)}$

Page 105 — Group 7 — The Halogens

Q1 a) false
b) true
c) false
d) true
Q2 The halogens exist as molecules — which are pairs of atoms.
A more reactive halogen — will displace a less reactive one.
The halogens react with metals — to form ionic compounds.
The reactivity of the halogens — decreases as you move down the group.
Q3 a) iron bromide
b) ionic bonding
Q4 a) Bromine is more reactive than iodine so displaces it from the potassium iodide solution. Bromine is less reactive than chlorine so doesn't displace it from potassium chloride solution.
b) $Br_{2(aq)} + 2KI_{(aq)} \rightarrow I_{2(aq)} + 2KBr_{(aq)}$

Chemistry 3a — Elements, Water and Organic Chemistry

Pages 106-107 — Transition Elements

Q1

Q2 less, higher, higher, harder, coloured, catalysts
Q3 high density
Q4 a) iron — ammonia production
nickel — converting oils into fats for making margarine
manganese(IV) oxide — decomposition of hydrogen peroxide
b) i) Fe^{2+}, Fe^{3+}
ii) Cu^+, Cu^{2+}
iii) Cr^{2+}, Cr^{3+}
Q5 a) crystals of different colours
b) The crystals won't be colourful. Only transition metals form coloured compounds.
Q6 Found in the block between Groups 2 and 3 of the periodic table.
Has a high melting point.
Has a high density.
Has a shiny appearance.
Forms coloured compounds.
Forms two different chlorides / forms ions with different charges.

Pages 108-109 — Hardness of Water

Q1 a) true
b) false
c) false
d) false
e) true
f) true
g) true
h) false
Q2 a) The kettle becomes less efficient / takes longer to boil.
b) E.g. calcium ions are good for healthy bones and teeth. / It could help reduce the risk of heart disease.
Q3 Permanent — Dissolved calcium sulfate
Temporary — Hydrogencarbonate ions
Q4 a) Ion exchange columns have lots of sodium or hydrogen ions which they exchange for calcium and magnesium ions, removing them from the water.
b) This works for both types of hardness.
Q5 a) calcium carbonate
b) i) A and B
ii) B
iii) A
iv) C
c) i) Permanent hardness is not removed by boiling.
ii) sodium carbonate (Na_2CO_3)/washing soda
d) i) Source A
ii) The reduction in the amount of soap needed to create a lather in water from this source after it had been boiled was the greatest.

Page 110 — Water Quality

Q1 a) distilled water
b) It is made by boiling water and condensing the steam which takes a lot of energy / is a very expensive process.
Q2 A — The water passes through a mesh screen to remove bits like twigs.
B — Chemicals are added to make solids and microbes stick together and fall to the bottom.
C — The water is filtered to remove all solids.
D — Chlorine is added to kill any remaining harmful microbes.

Q3 a) tooth decay, disease, cancer, bone, toxic
b) They could buy a water filter containing carbon.

Pages 111-112 — Reversible Reactions

Q1 products, react, reactants, balance, closed, escape
Q2 a) i) A, B
ii) AB
b) i) Y
ii) X
c) $A + B \rightleftharpoons AB$
d) at the same rate
Q3 a) True
b) False
c) True
d) False
Q4 a) It takes in heat because it must be endothermic.
b) backward
c) All reversible reactions are exothermic in one direction and endothermic in the other, so temperature will always change the position of equilibrium.
d) It will have no effect because both sides of the reaction have the same number of molecules/volume.
Q5 a) i) Forward, because there are three molecules on the left-hand side of the reaction and only two molecules on the right-hand side of the reaction.
ii) It moves it to the right / increases the amount of SO_3 produced.
b) B
c) It stays the same.

Page 113 — The Haber Process

Q1 a) $N_{2(g)} + 3H_{2(g)} \rightleftharpoons 2NH_{3(g)}$
b) E.g. air (nitrogen) and natural gas (hydrogen).
Q2 a) 200 atmospheres, 450 °C.
b) 1. High enough to give a good % yield.
2. Not so high that the plant becomes too expensive to build.
Q3 a) It will reduce the amount of ammonia formed.
b) To increase the rate of reaction.
c) They are recycled.
Q4 a) It has no effect on % yield.
b) It makes it cheaper to produce. The rate of reaction is increased without an expensive increase in temperature or pressure.

Pages 114-115 — Alcohols

Q1

Alcohol	No. of Carbon Atoms	Molecular Formula	Displayed Formula
Methanol	1	CH_3OH	H H–C–O–H H
Ethanol	2	C_2H_5OH	H H H–C–C–O–H H H
Propanol	3	C_3H_7OH	H H H H–C–C–C–O–H H H H

Q2 a) the −OH group
b) This shows the molecule's functional −OH group (and tells you more about the structure).
Q3 a) $C_2H_5OH_{(l)} + 3O_{2(g)} \rightarrow 2CO_{2(g)} + 3H_2O_{(g)}$
b) petrol, fuel, less, fermentation, renewable, land/sunshine, sunshine/land
Q4 a) False
b) False
c) True
d) False
e) True
f) True
g) True
Q5 dissolve, oils/fats, fats/oils, solvents, perfumes, oils, water

Chemistry 3b — Titrations, Energy and Chemical Tests

Q6 a) To stop people drinking it by mistake as it is toxic.
b) E.g. cleaning paint brushes and as a fuel

Page 116 — Carboxylic Acids

Q1 a) True
b) False
c) False

Q2

Carboxylic acid	No. of Carbon Atoms	Molecular Formula	Displayed Formula
Methanoic Acid	1	HCOOH	
Ethanoic Acid	2	CH_3COOH	
Propanoic Acid	3	C_2H_5COOH	

Q3 a) i) microbes
ii) oxidising agents
b) i) Carboxylic acids don't ionise completely so not many H^+ ions (responsible for making a solution acidic) are released.
ii) vinegar
c) lower

Page 117 — Esters

Q1 a) esters
b) don't, do
c) are
d) flammable, fire
e) -COO-

Q2

and methyl ethanoate

Q3 a) concentrated sulfuric acid
b) ethanol + **ethanoic acid** → ethyl ethanoate + **water**
Q4 a) Some esters are toxic, especially in large doses. / Some people worry about health problems with synthetic food additives.
b) E.g. perfumes

Pages 118-119 — Mixed Questions — Chemistry 3a

Q1 Any two from: e.g. they have pleasant smells. / They are volatile. / They mix well with other solvents.
Q2 a) Atomic mass
b) He left gaps for undiscovered elements.
c) 1
d) Group 2
Q3 a) $Cl_{2(aq)} + 2KBr_{(aq)} \rightarrow Br_{2(aq)} + 2KCl_{(aq)}$
b) Bromine is less reactive than chlorine, so it doesn't displace it from the solution.
Q4 a) $N_2 + 3H_2 \rightleftharpoons 2NH_3$
b) i) increase
ii) If you raise the pressure it encourages the reaction that produces less volume (molecules). The forward reaction produces less volume (molecules).
c) decrease
Q5 a) F.
Any two from: it has a high melting point. / It has a high density. / It is a good conductor of electricity.
b) It is used as a catalyst (transition metals make good catalysts).
Q6 a) i) Any one from: B, C or D
ii) E
iii) D
b) ionic, water, hydrogen, hydroxide

Q7 a) B
b) A
c) Boiling removes temporary hardness from water. River A must contain both permanent and temporary hardness. Once the temporary hardness was removed, less soap was needed to form a lasting lather.

Chemistry 3b — Titrations, Energy and Chemical Tests

Page 120 — Titration

Q1 a) i) Universal indicator changes colour gradually — titrations need a definite colour change.
ii) Any one from: e.g. phenolphthalein / methyl orange
b) Put some of the sodium hydroxide in a flask, along with some indicator.
Add the sulfuric acid, a bit at a time, to the sodium hydroxide using a burette — giving the flask a regular swirl. Go especially slowly (a drop at a time) when you think the sodium hydroxide's almost neutralised.
The indicator will change colour when it is.
Record the amount of sulfuric acid used to neutralise the sodium hydroxide.
Repeat this process a few times and take the mean of your results.
c)

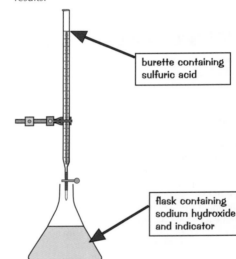

burette containing sulfuric acid

flask containing sodium hydroxide and indicator

Pages 121-122 — Titration Calculations

Q1 a) $2 \times 1 = 2$ moles
b) $1 \times (100 \div 1000) = 0.1$ moles
c) $0.1 \times (25 \div 1000) = 0.0025$ moles
d) $0.2 \times (10 \div 1000) = 0.002$ moles
Q2 a) $HCl + NaOH \rightarrow NaCl + H_2O$
b) $H_2SO_4 + 2\ KOH \rightarrow K_2SO_4 + 2H_2O$
Q3 a) i) $0.5 \times (23 + 16 + 1) = 20$ g
ii) $0.2 \times (2 + 32 + 64) = 19.6$ g
iii) $0.02 \times (40 + 32 + 2) = 1.48$ g
b) i) $0.1 \times (39 + 16 + 1) = 5.6$ g/dm³
ii) $2 \times (1 + 14 + 48) = 126$ g/dm³
Q4 a) $0.1 \times (20 \div 1000) = 0.002$ moles
b) $HCl + NaOH \rightarrow NaCl + H_2O$
c) From the equation, **1** mole of HCl reacts with **1** mole of NaOH
d) $0.002 \div 1 = 0.002$ moles
e) $0.002 \div (25 \div 1000) = 0.08$ mol/dm³
f) Concentration $= 0.08 \times (23 + 16 + 1) = 3.2$ g/dm³

Chemistry 3b — Titrations, Energy and Chemical Tests

Q5 a) i) Moles KOH = 0.1 × (30 ÷ 1000) = 0.003
ii) Reaction equation: $2KOH + H_2SO_4 \rightarrow K_2SO_4 + 2H_2O$, so 0.003 ÷ 2 = 0.0015 moles of H_2SO_4.
iii) Concentration of H_2SO_4 = 0.0015 ÷ (10 ÷ 1000) = 0.15 mol/dm³
b) Mass in grams = 0.15 × (2 + 32 + 64) = 14.7 g/dm³

Page 123 — Energy

Q1 energy, exothermic, heat, an increase, endothermic, heat, a decrease
Q2 a) 29.5 °C – 22 °C = **7.5 °C** (accept between 7 and 8 °C)
b) neutralisation, exothermic
c) Some energy is always lost to the surroundings.
Q3 a) break
b) formed
c) endothermic
d) exothermic
Q4 a) exothermic
b) A–C, because more energy is released when this bond forms than is used breaking the bond in A–B.

Page 124 — Energy and Fuels

Q1 a) Because copper is such a good conductor of heat.
b) Because heat energy is lost, e.g. in heating the can and the surrounding air.
Q2 a) Energy transferred = 50 × 4.2 × 30.5 = 6405 J
b) Energy per gram = 6405 ÷ 0.7 = 9150 J/g = 9.15 kJ/g
Q3 a) Energy transferred = 50 × 4.2 × 27 = 5670 J
Energy released per gram = 5670 ÷ 0.8 = 7087.5 J/g = 7.09 kJ/g
b) Petrol, because it releases more energy per gram of fuel than fuel X does.
Q4 a) E.g. carbon dioxide/CO_2
b) Any one from: e.g. global warming / climate change
c) As it is running out it will get more expensive. This means that everything that's transported by lorry, train or plane will get more expensive too.

Pages 125-126 — Bond Energies

Q1 a) A, C and D
b) B
c) B and E
d) C
Q2 a) endothermic
b) The minimum energy needed by reacting particles to break their bonds.
c) They speed up chemical reactions by providing a different pathway with a lower activation energy (so the reaction happens more easily and more quickly).
Q3 a) Energy change = –90 kJ/mol.
b) Activation energy = +70 kJ/mol.
c)

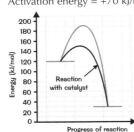

Q4 a) (4 × 412) + (2 × 498) = 2644 kJ/mol.
b) (2 × 743) + (4 × 463) = 3338 kJ/mol.
c) Energy change = 2644 – 3338 = –694 kJ/mol.

Q5 Energy needed to break bonds = [158 + (4 × 391) + 498] = 2220.
Energy released when bonds made = [945 + (4 × 463)] = 2797.
So overall energy change = 2220 – 2797 = –577 kJ/mol.
Q6 Energy needed to break bonds = [(2 × 348) + (12 × 412) + (7 × 498)] = 9126.
Energy released when bonds made = [(8 × 743) + (12 × 463) = 11 500.
So overall energy change = –2374 kJ/mol.

Page 127 — Getting Energy from Hydrogen

Q1 a) water
b) i) It is very clean as water isn't a pollutant.
ii) Any one from: e.g. you need a special, expensive engine. / You need energy from another source to make hydrogen. / Hydrogen's hard to store safely — it's very explosive.
Q2 fuel, oxygen, electricity
Q3 Fuel cell vehicles don't produce any pollutants — no greenhouse gases, no nitrogen oxides, no sulfur dioxide, no carbon monoxide. The only by-products are water and heat.
Q4 E.g. hydrogen is a gas so it takes up loads more space to store than liquid fuels like petrol. / It's very explosive so it's difficult to store safely. / The hydrogen fuel is often made either from hydrocarbons (from fossil fuels), or by electrolysis of water, which uses electricity (and that electricity's got to be generated somehow — usually this involves fossil fuels).

Pages 128-129 — Tests for Positive Ions

Q1 a) Metals **always** form positive ions.
b) Clean a wire loop by dipping it into hydrochloric acid and rinsing with distilled water. Then dip it in the sample, put it into the clear blue part of a Bunsen flame and observe any colours produced.
c) There could be other substances on the wire that might produce a different flame colour to the test substance.
Q2 a) red flame — Ca^{2+}
yellow flame — Na^+
crimson flame — Li^+
green flame — Ba^{2+}
lilac flame — K^+
b) potassium nitrate
Q3 a)

Positive Ion	Colour of Precipitate
Fe^{2+}	**green**
Cu^{2+}	blue
Fe^{3+}	**brown**
Al^{3+}	**white**

b) $Fe^{2+}_{(aq)} + 2OH^-_{(aq)} \rightarrow$ **$Fe(OH)_{2(s)}$**
c) $Fe^{3+}_{(aq)} + 3OH^-_{(aq)} \rightarrow$ **$Fe(OH)_{3(s)}$**
d) A white precipitate forms that then dissolves in excess NaOH to form a colourless solution.
Q4 a) $CuSO_4$
b) LiCl
c) $Al_2(SO_4)_3$
d) $FeSO_4$
e) $FeCl_3$
f) $CaCl_2$

<u>Chemistry 3b — Titrations, Energy and Chemical Tests</u>

<u>Page 130 — Tests for Negative Ions</u>

Q1 a) SO_4^{2-}
   b) I^-
   c) CO_3^{2-}

Q2   acid, carbon dioxide, limewater

Q3 a)   dilute hydrochloric acid, barium chloride solution
   b)   a white precipitate (of barium sulfate)

Q4   She could add dilute nitric acid to a solution of the compound, and then add some silver nitrate solution. If the compound contains Cl^- ions a white precipitate will form. If it contains Br^- ions a cream precipitate will form and if it contains I^- ions a yellow precipitate will form.

Q5 a) $Ag^+_{(aq)} + Cl^-_{(aq)} \rightarrow AgCl_{(s)}$
   b) $2HCl_{(aq)} + Na_2CO_{3(s)} \rightarrow 2NaCl_{(aq)} + H_2O_{(l)} + CO_{2(g)}$
   c) $Ba^{2+}_{(aq)} + SO_4^{2-}_{(aq)} \rightarrow BaSO_{4(s)}$

<u>Pages 131-132 — Mixed Questions — Chemistry 3b</u>

Q1 a)   An exothermic reaction. It gives out energy to the surroundings.
   b)   less than
   c)   E.g. burn the food or fuel and use the energy from the flame to heat up some water. Use the change in water temperature to find the amount of energy.
   d)   Energy transferred = $100 \times 4.2 \times 15 = 6300$ J
        Energy produced per gram = $6300 \div 0.5 = 12\,600$ J/g = 12.6 kJ/g

Q2 a)   He would see a green precipitate.
   b)   That the compound contains copper(II)/Cu^{2+} ions.
   c) $Cu^{2+}(aq) + 2OH^-(aq) \rightarrow Cu(OH)_{2(s)}$
   d)   He could add dilute hydrochloric acid/HCl to the compound, followed by barium chloride/$BaCl_2$ and look for a white precipitate.
   e) $CuSO_4$

Q3 a) and b)

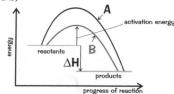

   c)   B
   d)   exothermic

Q4 a) Ca^{2+}
   b) CO_3^{2-}
   c) Fe^{3+}
   d) SO_4^{2-}

Q5 a)   Any one from: e.g. methyl orange / phenolphthalein
   b) i)   Moles NaOH = $0.5 \times (20 \div 1000) = 0.01$ moles
        NaOH + HCl $\rightarrow$ NaCl + H_2O, so there's also 0.01 moles of HCl.
        Concentration of HCl = $0.01 \div (25 \div 1000)$ = 0.4 mol/dm³
     ii) M_r HCl = $1 + 35.5. = 36.5$
        In 1 dm³: mass in grams = moles $\times M_r$ = 0.4×36.5 = 14.6 g/dm³

ISBN 978 1 84762 617 2

9 781847 626172

CAA44